We Learn All About
Endangered Species

A Complete Resource
for Preschool, Kindergarten,
and First Grade Teachers

by Sharon MacDonald

Fearon Teacher Aids
Simon & Schuster Education Group

Editorial Director: Virginia L. Murphy
Editor: Kristin Eclov
Copyeditor: Lisa Schwimmer
Illustration: Janet Skiles
Layout: Teena Remer
Production: Rebecca Speakes

ISBN 0-86653-944-1

Printed in the United States of America

1 . 9 8 7 6 5 4 3 2 1

Contents

To the Teacher

Dear Teacher:

In this book you will find everything you need to introduce endangered species into your classroom. It is a complete unit packed full of background information and learning activities that will help you teach children about endangered species.

The materials are presented in four sections—About Endangered Species, Vanishing Habitats, Animals in Danger, and We Can Help. You can pick and choose which topics you want to use. Each section contains an *introduction* and *activities*. The introductions give the basics of the topics, so there is little need for you to gather additional information on endangered species. The activities suggest projects for art time, snack time, play time, and learning time that correspond to and reinforce the topics. Since there are a number of activities listed for each topic, you can choose the ones that are appropriate for your class's skill level.

The *suggested reading* at the end of the teacher's guide lists reading and picture books that will enhance the children's enjoyment of endangered species. I suggest that when you introduce a topic, you also read one or two of the books to the children. You could also leave out picture books for the children to look at on their own.

The fourteen reproducible *worksheets* incorporate thinking and concept skills such as visual-discrimination skills and the fine-motor skills of drawing, cutting, and pasting. Suggestions for using the worksheets and the twenty-one reproducible *pattern pages* are included with the activities.

Have fun bringing endangered species to your classroom!

Sincerely,

Sharon MacDonald

TEACHER'S GUIDE

About Endangered Species

INTRODUCTION

Endangered animals are those whose populations have become so small that they are in danger of vanishing from the Earth. This drastic reduction in numbers is the beginning of a process called *extinction*. Extinction is sometimes a naturally occurring phenomenon. However, one of the principal reasons for extinction today is the destruction of animal habitats by human beings. The end result of this destruction is that all of the animals of a particular type, called a *species*, will die.

The most critical reason for extinctions is the expansion of human beings into previously untouched wilderness and human technology applied to these areas. For example, some rainforests are being destroyed for human use, including farming, lumber, and so on. Human expansion is encroaching on the animal habitats at a very rapid rate. In many parts of the world, human populations are growing so fast that there is not enough land and food supplies. Some animal species are in such danger of extinction that scientists have made a list of these animals, called the *endangered species list*. This list lets everyone know

About Endangered Species

which animals need special help from us if they are to survive. In other words, if people do not change their ways, these animal species will become extinct.

To understand extinction, think of the dinosaur. The dinosaur has vanished from the Earth. There are and will never be any more of them. While human existence played no part in the extinction of the dinosaur, their numbers are gone forever. There are other examples, too, such as the passenger pigeon. At one time, there were billions of passenger pigeons, but people hunted them for fun and ate them for food. The last passenger pigeon died in 1941. If people had been better informed about the danger of killing this species, its extinction could have been prevented. The endangered species list helps inform people about threatened animals so that this will not happen again.

Not only do we need to protect endangered animals, but we also need to save the wildlife habitats in which they live. Plants and animals help maintain the atmosphere's level of oxygen and carbon dioxide. Worms, insects, fungi, and bacteria recycle nutrients in the soils that we depend on for our crops. Plants help to regulate the flow of water and prevent floods. All of our food and most of our medicines are developed from plants and animals. If species continue to disappear, many will be gone before scientists have a chance to discover their possible benefits to humans.

All living things have a right to continue to exist. To be good stewards of the Earth, humans have the obligation to assure the survival of plant and animal life even if there is currently no known value to human beings. There is no need for plants and animals to become extinct because of human excess and insensitivity. Much of the pleasure of living comes from enjoying the wonderful variety and beauty of living things around us.

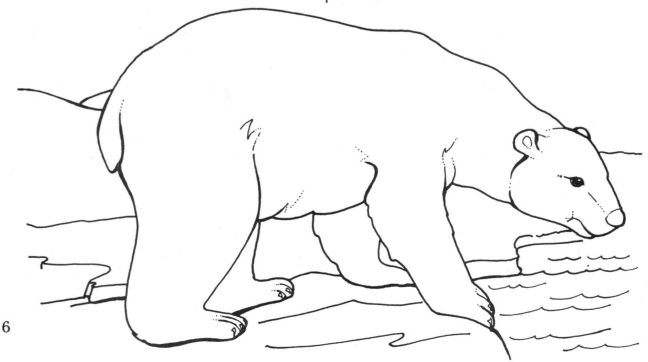

About Endangered Species

ACTIVITIES

❣ Take an environmental awareness walk around the neighborhood. Have the children look for items that are alive and items that are not. After returning to the classroom, list on the chalkboard all items the children saw. Then ask the children to sort the items into two categories—alive and not alive.

❣ Duplicate and hand out Worksheet 1 (page 39). Have the children sort the items that are alive from the items that are not.

❣ Make a class mural. Tape a long piece of butcher paper on a wall or fence. Give the children large paintbrushes and several buckets of water with blue or green food coloring added. Have the children paint the bottom half of the butcher paper green and the top half blue. Let the paper dry overnight. Have the children draw pictures of living things, such as elephants, tigers, and crocodiles, with colored markers on the painted background. Invite children to spend several days working on the mural, adding new pictures of living things each day. Encourage the children to include drawings of endangered species, too. Ask the children why they think it is important to keep plants and animals alive.

About Endangered Species

ACTIVITIES

❧ Take the children outside on a rock hunt. Look for all sizes, colors, shapes, and textures of rocks. Have the children sort the rocks by size, color, or shape. Talk about how rocks are made into soil by water erosion, wind erosion, or by being crushed. Have the children place the rocks in old socks and hit the rocks with a hammer. (Provide close adult supervision during this part of the activity.) Discuss with the children how easy or difficult it was to break open the rocks. Then invite the children to look at the insides of the rocks to see if there are any fossils. Look at the fragments with a magnifying glass. Then give the students several samples of soil to examine, too. Explain to the children that in nature, the rock fragments mix with decayed plant and animal life to become soil.

❧ Have students collect a variety of large rocks to use in a fossil hunt. Discuss with the children how fossils are formed. Fossils are generally impressions made in rock of plants and animals that lived thousands of years ago, such as dinosaurs. Fossils can give us important information about plants and animals that are now extinct. Set up a rock-breaking center outside on a hard, flat surface. Provide a hammer and several old socks for the children to use to break open the rocks. Place a rock inside a sock and show the children how to carefully hit the rock once or twice with a hammer. Be sure the children are under close adult supervision during this part of the activity. Encourage the children to examine the rocks to see if there are any fossils hidden inside.

About Endangered Species

ACTIVITIES

❦ Set up a work area outside to experiment with clay. Cover the table with plastic before this activity. Purchase potter's clay from a hobby shop or use clay from the ground (often found on river banks). Have the children experiment with using dry clay—rolling it, pounding it, cutting it with a plastic knife, and making imprints on it. Have the children work with wet clay as well. Have a water bowl nearby for the children to dip their hands into while working with the clay. Wet clay is easier to use. Encourage the children to make shell, leaf, rock, or twig imprints in the clay. Or, have children try to make endangered animal footprints in the clay using plastic spoons, popsicle sticks, or pencils. The book *Animal Footnotes* by Q.L. Pearce (Silver Press, 1990) is a good resource for footprint pictures. Explain to the students that the imprints are much like the fossils found inside rocks. If possible, bring some fossils to class to show the children. Set the clay imprints aside to dry completely. If you have access to a kiln, fire the children's creations. Use the garden hose to clean the work area.

❦ Take the children on a walk around the school grounds. Encourage the children to guess the ages of several trees. Then choose a mature tree. Explain to the children that you are going to measure around the trunk of the tree to discover its approximate age. First, have the children guess the age of the tree. Have two children wrap a piece of string around the outside of the tree trunk (at a height of about four feet from the ground). Have an adult helper cut the string to the width of the tree. Then measure the length of the string. Most trees grow about one inch in diameter a year. (Poplars grow too fast and Scotch Pine grow too slowly for this method to be reliable. Trees growing close together grow more slowly than a tree growing by itself. In most instances, the measurement will reasonably approximate the age of the tree.) Compare the guesses with the actual measurement.

About Endangered Species

ACTIVITIES

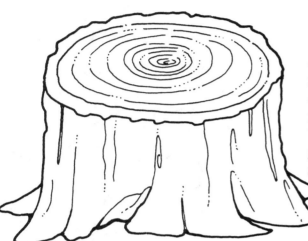

❣ If possible, show the children an old tree stump or a cross section from a mature tree. Point out the different rings that appear inside. Explain to the children that the rings can tell us a great deal of information about the tree. Each ring represents one year in the tree's life. A short distance between the rings tells us there wasn't much growth that year and a larger distance between rings tells us that there was adequate growth. Encourage each child to draw a cross section of a tree showing how old he or she is.

❣ Make a grass collage. Take the children on a nature walk around the neighborhood in search of different kinds of grass. Collect a variety of green grasses of different lengths and widths. Upon returning to the classroom, have the children glue the grasses to thin cardboard in interesting designs.

❣ Duplicate and hand out Worksheet 2 (page 40). Have the children discover the patterns in each row. Children cut out the squares of the endangered species that complete each pattern and paste them at the end of each row.

❣ Give each child a toilet-tissue tube to use to peek at a micro-environment. Take the children outside to a grassy area. Have the children look closely at the ground through the cardboard tubes. Encourage the children to dictate a list of all the items they see through the tubes. Then have the children look at the same area without using the tubes. Ask the students if it makes a difference whether or not they look through the cardboard tubes.

About Endangered Species

ACTIVITIES

❣ Give the children a variety of seeds to taste, such as popped popcorn, puffed wheat, peanuts, sunflower seeds, and pumpkin seeds. Then place raw peanuts, popcorn, and sunflower seeds in Ziploc bags with moistened paper towels. Label the bags and place them in a warm, sunny window. Encourage the children to observe whether the seeds sprout.

❣ Fill a dishpan with different grains, such as rice, wheat, rye, and oats. Have the children use the grains for mixing, pouring, and measuring with scoops, spoons, cups, and funnels.

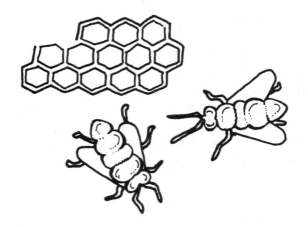

❣ Encourage the children to think of animals that help people. Write the list on the chalkboard. Then have the children match the animals with the ways they are helpful to human beings, such as bees making honey for people to eat. Even if the children are unable to read the words on the list it is important for them to see the relationship between the written and the spoken word.

❣ Have a zoo veterinarian come to school and talk to the children about taking care of endangered animals, such as rhinoceros, tigers, or elephants. Have the veterinarian explain some of the special needs of the different zoo animals. If possible, have the veterinarian bring a few small animals to class for the children to observe. Encourage the children to ask questions about the different animals.

❣ Teach the children the hand sign for "pigeon" as illustrated here.

Pigeon

11

Vanishing Habitats

INTRODUCTION

The most severe problem wildlife faces today is vanishing habitats. As human populations migrate and expand, water, land, and native plants that support wildlife populations are being diverted, claimed, and destroyed. When land is cleared for homes or farms, hundreds of animals must move to find new homes and surroundings. If similar habitats are close at hand, the animals make new homes and survive. If not, they may die. The animals may have trouble finding food to eat and shelter in which to raise their young. Sometimes if there is not enough protection, or if people live too close by, some animals stop having babies.

One example of the dangers of vanishing habitats is the marbled murrelet— a brown, penguin-like sea bird. The murrelet travels inland to the mountain forests to make its mossy nest high in the trees. They prefer the large, old coastal trees and these trees are being cut down to serve human needs. If a balance between human beings and wildlife isn't struck, the murrelets will soon be without a nesting area. It isn't the direct attack on the murrelets themselves that is the problem, but the assault on their surroundings—coastal trees—that places them at risk.

Water and food are essential to all life and there is natural competition for both. When people bring domesticated animals, like cows, sheep, or goats, to graze on the natural grasses, wild animals often are displaced or their food supplies are rapidly exhausted, leaving them nothing to eat. Even when the domesticated stocks are moved to other places to feed, the wild animals are left without food sources because the land has been over-grazed. Meat-eating animals, like the eagle, need large, isolated areas on which to feed and survive. If these areas become too small, they may starve or their reproductive cycle will become disrupted because they will not mate.

There are other ways of destroying habitats as well. Sometimes, people use poisons in the environment to control pests. Some of these pests are killed and eaten by other animals and they, in turn, become sick or die. The poisons remain in the environment, affecting animal life,

Vanishing Habitats

disturbing reproduction, and contaminating water sources and the fish that live in them. Birds eat the fish and become sick. The brown pelican, for example, was endangered for awhile because of the poison in the water. The brown pelican is the smallest of all pelicans and it is the only plunge-diving pelican in the world. Pelicans lay their eggs at the same nesting site every year, but they will not lay eggs at the same site if the water around has

been polluted. At one time, humans used a poison called *DDT* to control pests. Many bird species were threatened with extinction because of its use. The eagle and the brown pelican are two examples. When DDT was banned from use, these bird populations began to make a comeback.

Some animals have a very limited diet and they will eat only a certain type of plant. The panda bear in China is a good example. It faces extinction today because the bamboo plant on which it feeds is in a cycle of decline in many areas in China. This decline is brought about by the life cycle of bamboo itself. Large areas of bamboo spontaneously die every one hundred years. Scientists do not yet understand why. Adding to this, bamboo is harvested for human uses. These two unrelated events have greatly reduced the amount of bamboo available for food for the panda, and its numbers have declined.

If humans continue to plow and harvest plants used by wildlife without regard for what effects these actions have on animal populations, many animals may starve. We need to become aware that there are relationships between all living things and their surroundings, which must be preserved. These interrelationships must be understood if we are to save our natural surroundings and the plant and animal populations that thrive in them.

Vanishing Habitats

ACTIVITIES

❣ Duplicate and hand out the pattern on page 55. Encourage the children to decorate the bird using crayons or markers to make a colorful parrot sitting in a tree. Then have an adult helper cut a toilet-tissue tube in half for each child. Glue the completed parrots to the cardboard tubes. Place a tree branch in a coffee can and pour mixed plaster of paris around the base of the branch. When the plaster is dry, slide the parrots onto the branches. Display the tree of parrots in the classroom.

❣ Have an adult helper cut new sponges into a variety of animal-footprint shapes. Glue thread spools or pieces of dowel to the backs of sponges for handles. Have the children dip the sponges into shallow pie tins of tempera paint and carefully press the sponges on large sheets of paper to create a trail of animal footprints.

❣ If there is a botanical garden, arboretum, zoo, or wildlife refuge in the area, plan a field trip to see it. Point out how many zoos and wildlife refuges try to provide natural habitats for each species. Encourage the children to discuss the different plants and animals they see on the field trip.

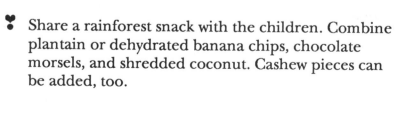

❣ Share a rainforest snack with the children. Combine plantain or dehydrated banana chips, chocolate morsels, and shredded coconut. Cashew pieces can be added, too.

Vanishing Habitats

ACTIVITIES

❣ Bring an old bird's nest to school for the children to examine. Then cut the nest in half so that the children can see a cross section. Talk about the materials the birds used to make the nest. Discuss what would happen if birds were unable to find materials to make their nests.

❣ Bring in several abandoned animal and insect homes for the children to look at. Have a magnifying glass or two for the children to use to examine the different homes more closely. The easiest ones to find are bird's nests, wasp nests, and dirt-dobber nests. Be sure to warn the children not to pick up a nest that has fallen to the ground without adult supervision.

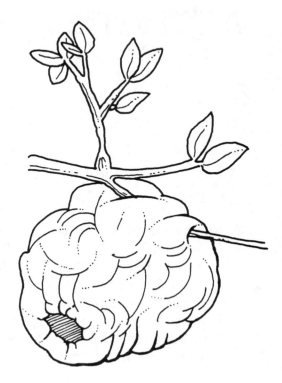

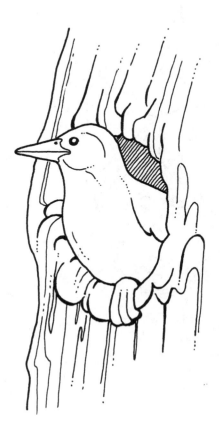

❣ Duplicate and hand out Worksheet 3 (page 41). Have the children color the picture and cut on the dotted lines to make a puzzle.

❣ Encourage the children to think of what it would be like to be an animal looking for a place to live. Ask the children what they would do if they discovered there were too many people living nearby, or there was no water, trees, or food in the area. Ask the children to think about what animals probably do when they are faced with the same problems.

Vanishing Habitats

ACTIVITIES

❣ Place a white bed sheet under a bush and then gently shake the bush to see what creatures may fall out. Encourage the children to carefully observe the insects for a few minutes without touching them. Talk about what kinds of creatures depend on the bush for food or shelter. Invite the children to write or dictate stories about what it would be like to live in a bush. Encourage the students to include illustrations with their stories.

❣ Make a net for catching insects or other creatures. Have an adult helper bend a coat hanger into a round shape. Stretch the top of a nylon stocking around the coat-hanger circle and tape securely— the foot of the stocking will hang loosely. Place any insects that are caught in jars with holes in the lids. Encourage the children to observe the insects for a short time and then let the creatures go free.

❣ Use the patterns provided on pages 56-57 to create a crocodile seriation. Duplicate the patterns, color them, and then glue the patterns on tagboard. Help the children order the crocodiles from the smallest to the largest.

❣ In separate containers of water, add dirt, vinegar, salt, tea, or coffee. Then pour each mixture through a coffee filter and label it. Allow the filters to dry. Then look at each one and compare the contents. Encourage the children to describe what was in the water and on the filter. Use a large sheet of paper to record the students' responses. Discuss with the children the importance of having clean water for animals as well as people.

Vanishing Habitats

ACTIVITIES

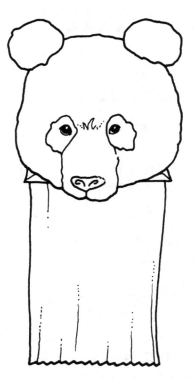

❧ Spread Vaseline on several sheets of white construction paper. Set the pieces of paper in several different places, such as in the classroom, outdoors, under a tree, and close to a street. Label each piece of paper with its location. Leave the papers in place for two days to see what sticks to the Vaseline. Ask the children to examine the papers and then discuss with the children the results of their experiment.

❧ Have each child walk like an animal to music. Encourage the other children in the class to guess which animal each child is portraying.

❧ Make animal paper-bag puppets. Duplicate and hand out the patterns on pages 58-59. Have the children color and cut out the animal faces. Give each child a paper lunch bag. Then help the children glue the animal faces to the bottoms of each bag. Show the children the pictures in the book *Endangered Animals* (National Wildlife Federation, 1989). Encourage interested children to color their puppets to look like real animals.

❧ Invite the children to feed the birds every day. Experiment with various types of food, such as nuts, bread, and seeds, to see what kinds of birds come to eat. Encourage the students to keep track of the number of birds that come to eat each day, too.

Vanishing Habitats

ACTIVITIES

❧ Duplicate and hand out Worksheet 4 (page 42). Have the children help the panda bear find bamboo to eat.

❧ Create a habitat for birds and small animals in a quiet spot on the school grounds. Have the children bring leaves, logs, discarded Christmas trees, branches, and grass to school. Arrange the items in a pile so that small animals can hide inside. Sprinkle seeds over the area and set out pans of water, as well. Place a sign close by the habitat announcing "QUIET—Home for Small Animals."

❧ Have the children spread peanut butter on round rice cakes and then arrange raisins to make animal footprints. Encourage the children to look at the prints and describe the type of animals that might make them. Then enjoy the peanut butter and rice cake snacks with your students.

❧ Teach the children the hand sign for "bear" as illustrated here.

❧ Duplicate and hand out Worksheet 5 (page 43). Have the children count the items in each row. Children then cut out the numbers and paste them in the correct boxes.

Bear

Animals in Danger

INTRODUCTION

There are many animals that make good pets—dogs, cats, and some birds, to name a few. But most animals are not able to adapt to a pet lifestyle. Wild animals do not make good pets, but some people still enjoy having unusual pets.

The demand for unusual, exotic animals is massive. Thousands of animals are removed from the wild each year and sold to animal dealers who in turn sell them to others who eventually place them with eager buyers. Unfortunately, the most exotic animal is also the most rare and endangered. When an endangered animal is removed from the wild, there is one less animal available to participate in reproducing its own kind, and the species is pushed closer to extinction. The only good places for wild animals in captivity are in special settings, like zoos, where

the animals' needs are met and the requirements for their happiness and survival are known. Every year, more than 7 million wild birds are trapped to be sold as pets. Many of them do not survive or even make it to pet stores. They die in transit.

There are other reasons why humans capture wild animals. Animals that have unusual skins or horns are sometimes hunted. Pythons and other beautiful snakes are killed so their skins can be made into belts and boots. Alligator skin is valuable for the same reason. The American alligator was placed on the endangered species list because people were killing them in great numbers for their skins. After people learned that they were endangered, they stopped buying things made from alligator skins and the alligator is now no longer on the endangered species list.

Animals in Danger

Similarly, some people like to wear fur coats made from animal skins, like the snow leopard, lynx, and ocelot. Trappers

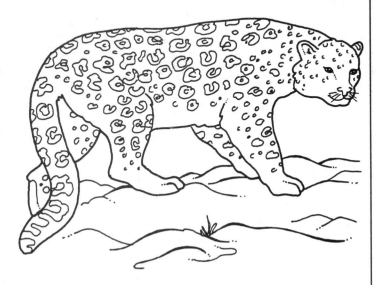

and hunters have killed too many of these animals and they are threatened and endangered at the present time. It is hoped that people will stop buying these furs, thereby reducing the demand which makes it profitable to hunt and trap them.

Other animals are hunted for special qualities they possess. For example, elephants are killed for their ivory tusks to make jewelry and carvings. The tusks cannot be taken from the elephants without killing them. Some animals are endangered because people think that parts of their bodies have magic powers.

Rhinoceros horns are ground into powder that is said to cure high fevers. Rhinoceros must be killed to get the horns as well.

Some animals are hunted because they are very rare. These animals, like the mountain gorilla or the bighorn sheep, are made into trophies. Zebra skin is also used as decoration. Some whales are endangered because too many have been killed for their body parts, for everything from perfume to fertilizer to dog food. Whalers are learning that they are killing too many whales and are working on ways to keep the right whale, sie whale, blue whale, and humpback whale from becoming extinct. All of these animals are on the endangered species list and need to be protected.

Animals in Danger

ACTIVITIES

❣ Make animal books for the children to use for creating illustrations and writing stories. Enlarge and then duplicate the animal patterns on pages 60-69. Place writing paper behind each pattern before cutting out the animal shape. Encourage the children to write or dictate animal stories to include in their books. Invite children to color the front animal pattern as well.

❣ Collect a variety of animal cookie cutters. Make playdough and encourage the children to make animal shapes with the cookie cutters in the playdough center.

Playdough Recipe

1 cup flour	1/2 cup salt
2 tsp cream of tartar	1 Tbsp oil
1 cup water	food coloring (optional)

In a bowl, mix together all the ingredients using a whisk. Pour the mixture in an electric skillet and cook at 350° until the mixture is a solid lump. Be sure to cook out of reach of the children. The mixture should pull away from the sides of the skillet into a firm ball. Have an adult helper knead the dough until it cools and then store the dough in a covered plastic container or resealable plastic bag.

❣ Duplicate and hand out Worksheet 6 (page 44). Have the children cut out the different sizes of animals and paste them in order from largest to smallest.

Animals in Danger

ACTIVITIES

❣ Collect a variety of fake fur pieces. Use the patterns provided on pages 60-69 to make animal-shaped collages. Trace the patterns onto 8 1/2" x 11" pieces of cardboard. Encourage the children to cover the animal silhouettes with fake fur.

❣ Create an animal-word writing box. Write the names of several animals on sentence strips and then glue a picture or plastic representation of that animal beside the written word. Place the word strips in a shoebox or cigar box with pencils and paper. Encourage the children to practice writing the animal words and then using the words in animal stories.

❣ Cut easel paper into the shape of an elephant by enlarging and then tracing the pattern on page 70. Invite the children to paint the large elephant canvases.

Animals in Danger

ACTIVITIES ❣

❣ Gather a variety of textured materials, such as screen, burlap, foil, mesh, bubble packing material, and crumpled grocery bags. Have the children place previously used paper over the different textures and rub crayons on them to create designs. Discuss with the children the variety of textures of different animals' skins, such as snakes, lions, rhinoceros, crocodiles, and whales.

❣ Cut several squares of 1" x 1" fake fur. Attach clothespins to the back sides of the fur pieces as handles. Encourage the children to experiment with using the fur pieces as paintbrushes. Display the fur prints in the classroom.

❣ Duplicate and hand out Worksheet 7 (page 45). Have the children match the animals to their shadows.

❣ Mix up a batch of "jewelry dough" to make animal necklaces.

Jewelry Dough

1 cup cornstarch   2 cups baking soda
1 1/4 cups cold water

Blend the ingredients in a saucepan. Cook for 4 minutes over medium heat, stirring constantly, until the mixture thickens and clings to the spoon. Wet a dish towel and cover the mixture while it is cooling. When it is cool enough to touch, knead the dough well. Break off pieces for the children to use and keep the remaining dough damp with wet toweling. Roll out the dough and use animal cookie cutters to make pendants, or the children can make free-form animal jewelry. The dough dries quickly, so make only as much as you will be using. When the dough has dried, the jewelry can be painted.

Animals in Danger

ACTIVITIES

❣ Cut several 2' x 2' squares of fake fur. Sew or staple 1/4" pieces of elastic from corner to corner on each square. Invite the children to strap the fur pieces on their backs and pretend to be animals. Encourage the children to walk, hop, run, and sleep like different animals. Discuss what it feels like to act like an animal. Ask the students what animal they would like to be if they had a choice. Encourage each child to draw a picture of his or her animal.

❣ Have animal crackers for a snack. Help the children graph the number of different animals in the animal-cracker box on the chalkboard.

❣ Duplicate and hand out Worksheet 8 (page 46).

❣ Make animal-shaped crayons. Have the children peel the paper from a variety of colors of crayons. Melt one color of crayon at a time in a microwave-safe glass container. Pour the melted wax into an animal-shaped candy mold. The crayon wax will cool quickly and can be removed to make different colors. Encourage the children to use the new crayons to create wild animal pictures to decorate the classroom walls.

❣ Make endangered animals with moveable legs. Enlarge the animal patterns provided on pages 71-74. Trace and cut out the pattern pieces on tagboard for durability. Make several sets of each pattern for tracing. Younger children may need the patterns duplicated directly onto construction paper. Have the older children trace and cut out the animal patterns on construction paper. Help the children use paper fasteners to attach the legs to the body of each animal. Display the animals around the classroom.

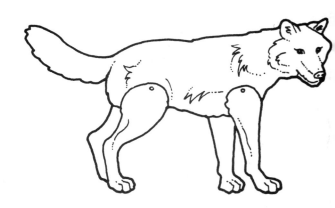

Animals in Danger

ACTIVITIES

❣ Teach the children the hand sign for "elephant" as illustrated here.

❣ Explain to the children that many birds naturally shed their old feathers in order to grow new feathers. Gather a variety of feathers and use them for paintbrushes at the easel. Encourage the children to experiment with the different kinds of feathers.

❣ Collect several turkey feathers to use as quills at the writing table. Invite the children to dip the pointed ends in a small container of black tempera paint. Then show the children how to use the quills as pens.

Elephant

❣ Read the book *The Great Kapok Tree* by Lynne Cherry (Harcourt Brace Jovanovich, 1990). Challenge the children to count the number of rainforest creatures on each page. Discuss why the kapok tree was so important to the animals.

❣ Duplicate and hand out Worksheet 9 (page 47). Have the children follow the letters of the alphabet to discover the hidden picture.

We Can Help

INTRODUCTION

We can save animals and their habitats if we are willing to work at it. Animals need the protection of their natural surroundings and homes. They need to be safe from hunters and other people who claim their lands for industry, ranching, farming, and residential uses. Animals need the protection of laws to keep people from selling them and buying wild animals as pets. In many parts of the world, laws are also necessary to keep people from buying animal furs, skins, and other animal parts, like the tusks of elephants and walrus.

It is helpful to know which animals are threatened in your area. Contact the United States Fish and Wildlife Service in your area for this information. They have a list of animals that are endangered in each geographic region. Learn about these animals and what can be done to help them survive. Then teach someone else about them. Learning about the habits of animals and the habitats in which they thrive, and then sharing your knowledge with others, will make it possible for humans and animals to live together. Sometimes, letting important people know how you feel about animals can bring these creatures back from near extinction.

Write a class letter to the Senator or Representative of your state to let them know you care about animals and that you want laws enacted to help save them. Doing this can make a difference. In 1903, fewer than 1,000 bison existed. The bison were killed in great numbers and the lands on which they ranged were homesteaded and fenced. The best

grasslands on which they roamed and fed were used for domesticated stock, like cattle, and many areas became over-grazed. In many places, the bison starved to death. After people learned what was happening to the bison, they protested, and laws were passed to protect the bison. Now there are more than 80,000 bison roaming the North American plains.

We Can Help

Many zoos are working to save animals from extinction. While extinction is sometimes a naturally occurring process, it is happening now at an alarming rate. Many zoos are attempting to slow this process by raising endangered species and then releasing them later in the wild. Other animals raised in zoos are on the edge of extinction and these animals would not survive if they were returned to the wild. Scientists learn more about endangered animals by studying them and learning about the foods they eat, their habits, and their habitats. They have come to learn what the animals need. Whooping cranes, for example, were on the endangered species list for a long time. Scientists learned that cranes lay two eggs, but only one of the eggs is raised as a chick. Now scientists remove the extra egg from the nests and raise the baby chick to a point where it can be released in the wild. In 1950, there were only about 21 whooping cranes alive in the world. Now, there are approximately 220 "whoopers" surviving in their natural habitat because people helped.

The easiest way to help save endangered wildlife is to get the facts on the environmental problems these creatures face. We can help in our everyday lives, both at home and at school. We need to use natural resources more wisely and stop wasting electricity, water, and heat. That way, we do not have to take more land and animal habitats for electric power-plants, dams, and mines. We need to recycle as much as possible to help the plants and animals that are threatened by our mounting piles of trash and garbage in landfills, our poorly planned land developments, and our industrial waste and pollution. Conservation at home and at school can help save endangered species everywhere.

We Can Help

ACTIVITIES

❣ Take the children on a field trip to visit the zoo. Look for the signs that point out endangered species. Discuss with the children the different animals that are considered endangered and try to learn as much as possible about them at the zoo. Point out on a world map (page 75) the countries where the different endangered species live.

❣ Duplicate and hand out Worksheet 10 (page 48). Have the children sort the animals that would make good pets from the animals that would not.

❣ Purchase a tub of plastic zoo and farm animals for the children to sort. Put a picture of a zoo animal on one tray and a picture of a farm animal on another. Have the children sort the animals according to where they can be seen—in a zoo or on a farm.

We Can Help

ACTIVITIES

❣ Encourage the children to create two types of zoos in the block area—one with cages and one with large enclosed areas. Give the children plastic berry baskets to use for "cages" as well as other zoo buildings. Discuss the advantages and disadvantages of the two zoo types.

❣ Give the children pieces of green and blue material and small plastic trees to create natural habitats for a different kind of zoo. Give the children a variety of plastic animals to play with in the two different zoo habitats. Encourage the children to talk about what it would be like to be in both kinds of habitats. Explain that many zoos try to recreate environments that are similar to the animals' natural habitats. This type of zoo allows visitors to see each animal's behavior in a more natural setting.

❣ Have the children write a class letter to an organization that supports wildlife, such as Worldwide Fund for Nature, to find out more information about the work they do to protect the animals of the world. The Worldwide Fund for Nature has campaigned to protect the world's habitats and wildlife since 1961. The address to write to is:

Worldwide Fund for Nature
1250 24th Street NW
Washington, DC 20037

We Can Help

ACTIVITIES

❣ Invite a guest speaker who is interested in protecting plants and animals to visit the classroom. Help the children prepare several questions ahead of time to ask the special visitor. After the visit, have the children write thank-you notes to the guest speaker.

❣ Send home notes to parents explaining simple things that their families can do to help protect wildlife. Provide a list of organizations where families can get more information.

Kids for Saving Earth
P.O. Box 47247
Plymouth, MN 55447-0247

The Environmental Defense Fund
1616 P Street NW, Suite 150
Washington, DC 20036

Defenders of Wildlife
1244 19th Street NW
Washington, DC 20036

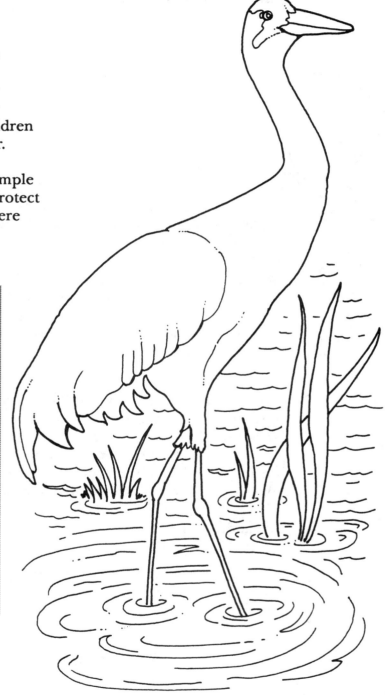

We Can Help

ACTIVITIES

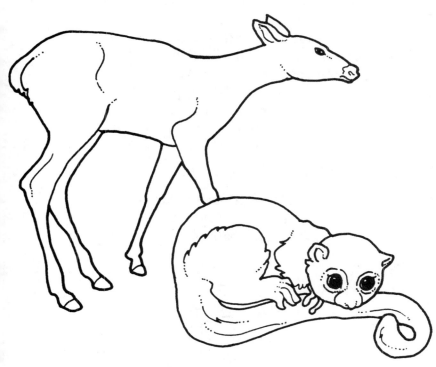

❣ Make an endangered species bulletin board using several of the patterns provided on pages 60-69. There are approximately 800 creatures on the endangered species list. Encourage the children to include other examples of endangered species, too. Help the children trace the patterns on construction paper and then color the patterns with crayons or markers. Have the children cut out the animal shapes and help staple the shapes to the bulletin board. Encourage the children to write or dictate, on 5" x 9" recipe cards, any information they would like to share about their endangered species pictures. Use a copy of the world map provided on page 75 to show where each species lives.

❣ Have the children cut out a variety of pictures of animals from magazines to make a large class animal collage. Overlap the pictures until there is no background paper showing. Then have the children go through and try to find any animal that they have learned about that is endangered.

❣ Duplicate and hand out Worksheet 11 (page 49). Have the children follow the dotted lines from the animals to their favorite foods.

We Can Help

ACTIVITIES

❣ Fill a water table with sand, rocks, leaves, twigs, and plastic animals. Encourage the children to use their imaginations as they play with the various materials.

❣ Read *Chickens Aren't the Only Ones* by Ruth Heller (Grosset & Dunlop, 1981). The book is written in rhyme and it describes many of the creatures that lay eggs— chickens, birds, reptiles, amphibians, fish, and insects. The word *oviparous* (egg laying) is introduced to the children. Encourage the children to brainstorm what would happen if all of these animals and insects did not lay their eggs because there was no place to lay them. Record the students' responses on the chalkboard.

❣ Duplicate and hand out Worksheet 12 (page 50). Have the children match the mothers with their babies.

We Can Help

ACTIVITIES

❣ Have the children create animal silhouettes. Tape a large sheet of butcher paper on the wall. Shine the light from a slide projector or overhead projector on the paper. Have the children stand between the light and the paper, making a shadow. Invite the children to pose in different ways to make themselves look like different animals. When each student has made an animal that he or she likes, have a partner trace around the shadow with a black marker. The shadows can overlap or they can be cut out and glued to a black sheet of paper.

❣ Duplicate and hand out Worksheet 13 (page 51). Have the children cut out the pictures of the animals and glue them in the correct boxes displaying the animals' homes.

❣ Have the children release an eyedropper full of watery, black tempera paint onto sheets of white construction paper. Have the children fold their papers in half and run their fingers up and down the folded pages a few times. Then have each child open his or her paper to see the pretend animals. Invite the children to name their imaginary animals and tell what kind of habitat they might live in.

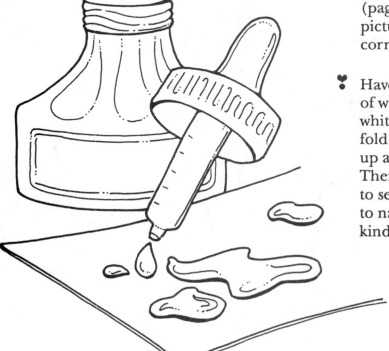

We Can Help

ACTIVITIES

Protect the Pandas

❣ Duplicate and hand out Worksheet 14 (page 52). Have the children discover the hidden picture.

❣ Make endangered species posters using the patterns provided on pages 60-69. Enlarge the patterns and hand out copies to the children. Help children trace the patterns on sheets of 11" x 17" construction paper. Discuss with the children the importance of protecting endangered species and their habitats. Have the children write or dictate messages on their posters about saving the different creatures of the world.

❣ Teach the children the hand signs that spell the word "zoo" as illustrated here.

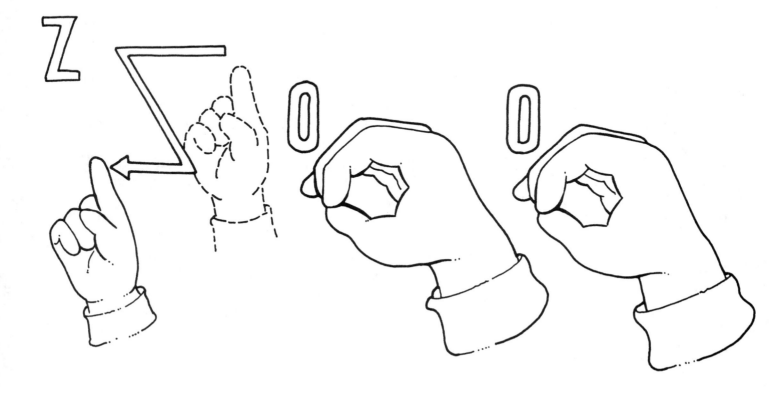

Suggested Reading

Baylor, Byrd. *Hawk, I'm Your Brother.* New York: Charles Scribner's Sons, 1976. (1-2)

Cherry, Lynne. *The Great Kapok Tree.* New York: Harcourt Brace Jovanovich, 1990. (1-2)

Cowcher, Helen. *Rain Forest.* New York: Farrar, Straus and Giroux, 1988. (K-1)

Endangered Animals. Washington, D.C.: National Wildlife Federation, 1989. (Resource)

Heller, Ruth. *Chickens Aren't the Only Ones.* New York: Grosset & Dunlop, 1981. (K-1)

Jeffers, Susan. *Brother Eagle, Sister Sky.* New York: Dial Books, 1991. (K-1)

Jordan, Tanis. *Journey of the Red-Eyed Tree Frog.* San Marcos, CA: Green Tiger Press, 1992. (PS-2)

Pearce, Q.L. and W.J. *Animal Footnotes.* Englewood Cliffs, NJ: Silver Press, 1991. (PS-1)

Pearce, Q.L. and W.J. *In the African Grasslands.* Englewood Cliffs, NJ: Silver Press, 1990. (PS-1)

Pearce, Q.L. and W.J. *In the Desert.* Englewood Cliffs, NJ: Silver Press, 1990. (PS-1)

Pearce, Q.L. and W.J. *In the Forest.* Englewood Cliffs, NJ: Silver Press, 1990. (PS-1)

Rice, Paul and Peter Mayle. *As Dead As A Dodo.* Boston: David Godien, 1981. (Resource)

Seuss, Dr. *The Lorax.* New York: Random House, 1971. (PS-1)

Stone, Lynn M. *Endangered Animals.* Chicago: Childrens Press, 1984. (1-2)

The Earth Works Group. *50 Simple Things Kids Can Do To Save The Earth.* New York: Andrews and McMeel, 1990. (Resource)

Thornhill, Jan. *The Wildlife 1 2 3.* New York: Simon & Schuster Children's Books, 1992. (PS-K)

Turner, Ann. *Heron Street.* New York: Harper & Row, 1989. (K-1)

STUDENT
WORKSHEETS

Name _____

Cut and then paste the pictures
in the correct boxes.

Alive

Not Alive

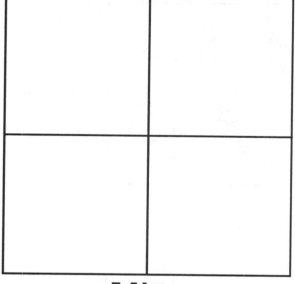

feather   snail

bird   book

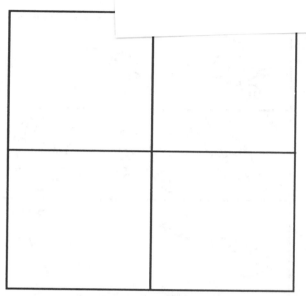

glasses   tree

shoe   flower

Skills: sorting and grouping, fine motor (cutting and pasting)

Name _____

Look at each row. Find the pattern. Cut and then paste the picture that completes the pattern at the end of each row.

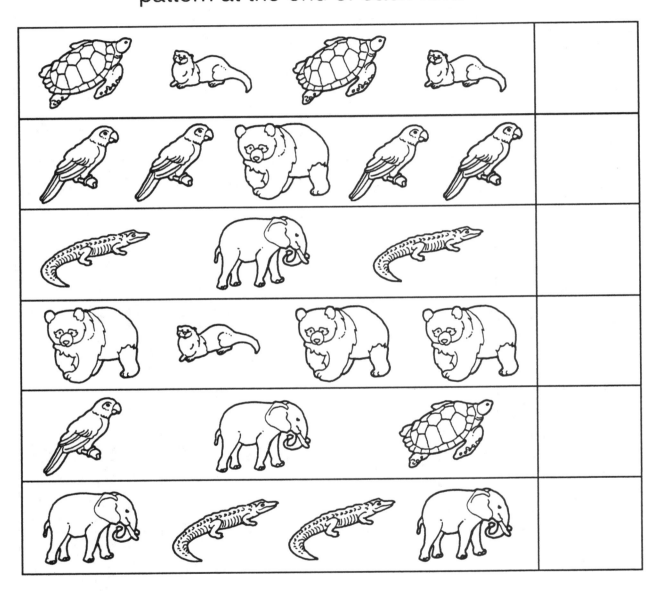

Name _____

Make a puzzle. Color the picture.
Cut on the dotted lines.

Name _____

Help the panda bear find the bamboo.
Do not cross any lines.

Name _____

Count the animals in each row. Cut and then paste the correct number in each box.

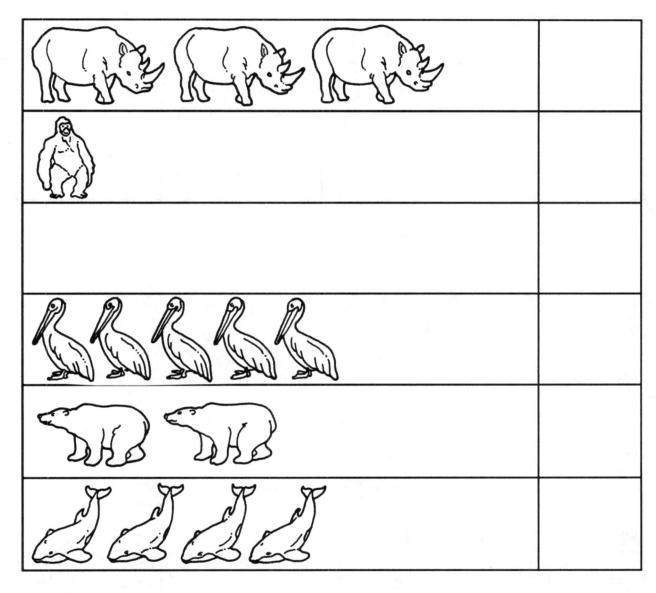

✂

| 0 | 1 | 2 | 3 | 4 | 5 |

Name _____

Cut out the animal cards. Paste the cards in order from largest to smallest.

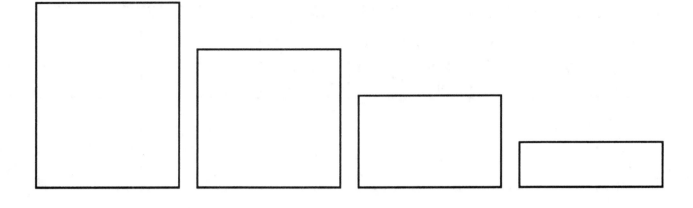

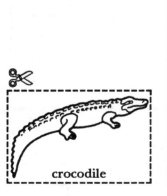

crocodile

whale

black-footed ferret

rhinoceros

44   Skills: size awareness, fine motor (cutting and pasting)

Name _____

Cut and then paste the shadows
in the correct boxes.

pigeon	buffalo	whale	butterfly

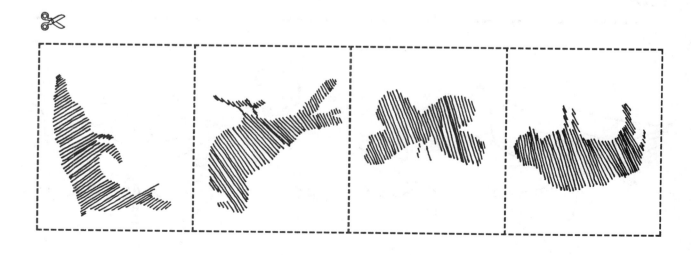

Skills: visual discrimination, matching, fine motor (cutting and pasting)   45

Name _____

In each row, find the bird that is different.
Circle it.

Skills: understanding the concept of different, visual discrimination, fine motor (drawing)

We Learn All About Endangered Species © 1993 Fearon Teacher Aids

Name _____

Connect the dots in order from A to Z.

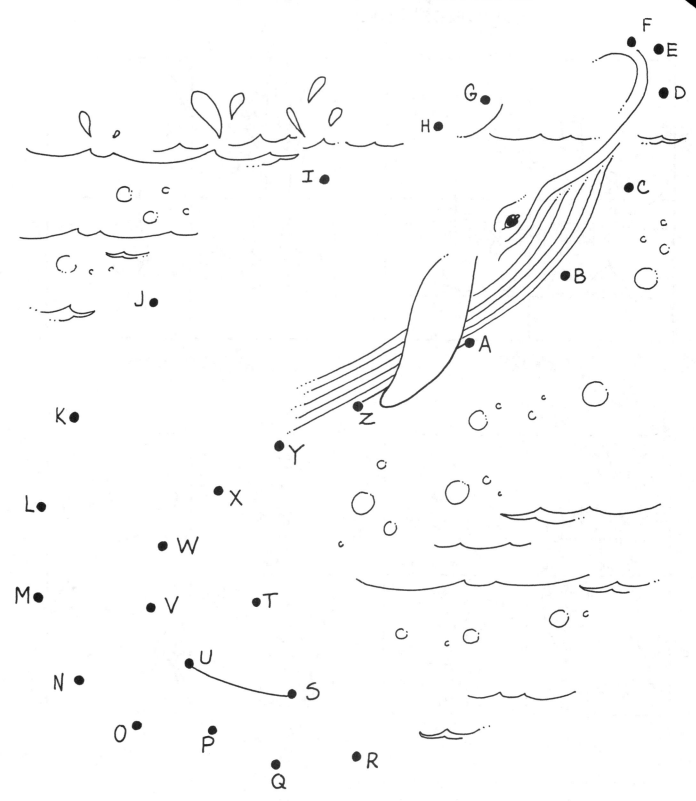

ıe _____

ι and then paste the pictures
the correct boxes.

Pets

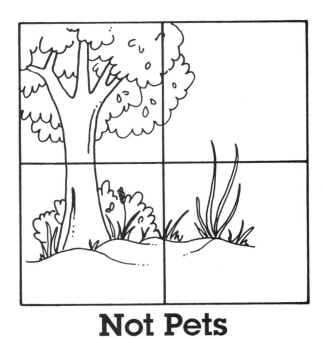

Not Pets

lion   goldfish

cat   panda bear

toucan   gerbil

whale   horse

Skills: sorting and grouping, fine motor (cutting and pasting)

48

Name _____

Follow each set of footprints to the food.
Trace each dotted line without lifting your pencil.

Name _____

Draw lines matching the mothers with their babies.

Skills: visual discrimination, fine motor (drawing)

We Learn All About Endangered Species © 1993 Fearon Teacher Aids

Name _____

Cut and then paste the pictures in the correct boxes.

bird's nest	ocean	tree in rainforest	plains

✂

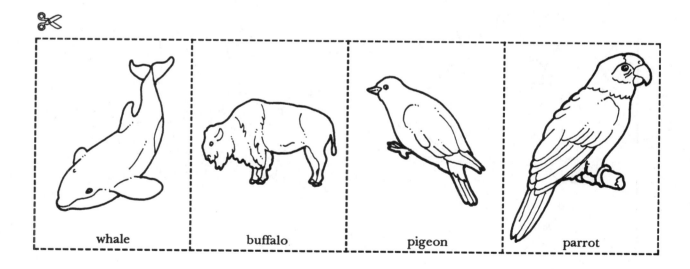

whale	buffalo	pigeon	parrot

Name _____

Color the spaces these colors:
  1 = orange   3 = green
  2 = black   4 = white

We Learn All About Endangered Species © 1993 Fearon Teacher Aids

PATTERN PAGES

Parrot Pattern

55

Crocodile Pattern

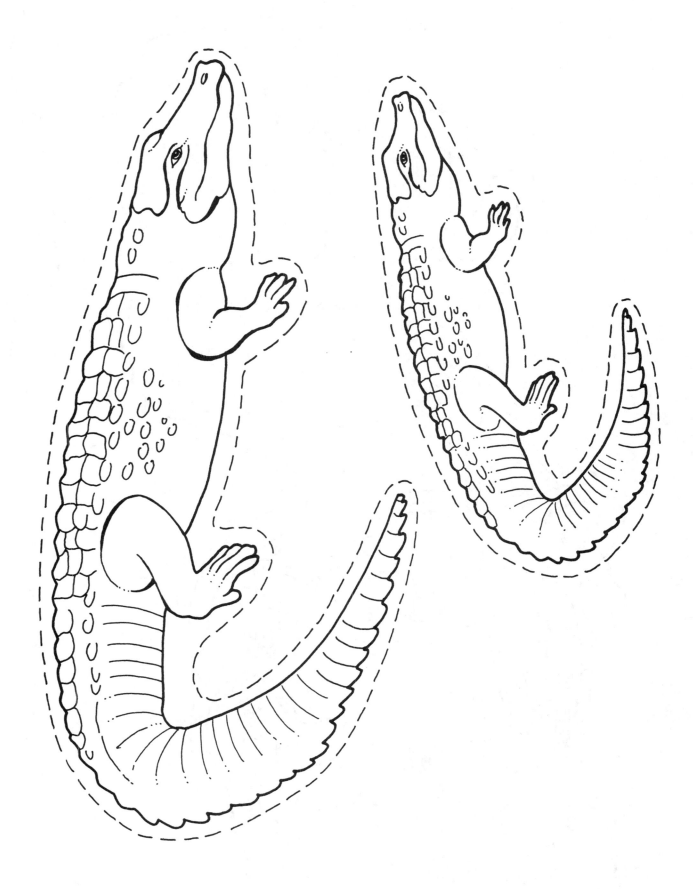

We Learn All About Endangered Species © 1993 Fearon Teacher Aids

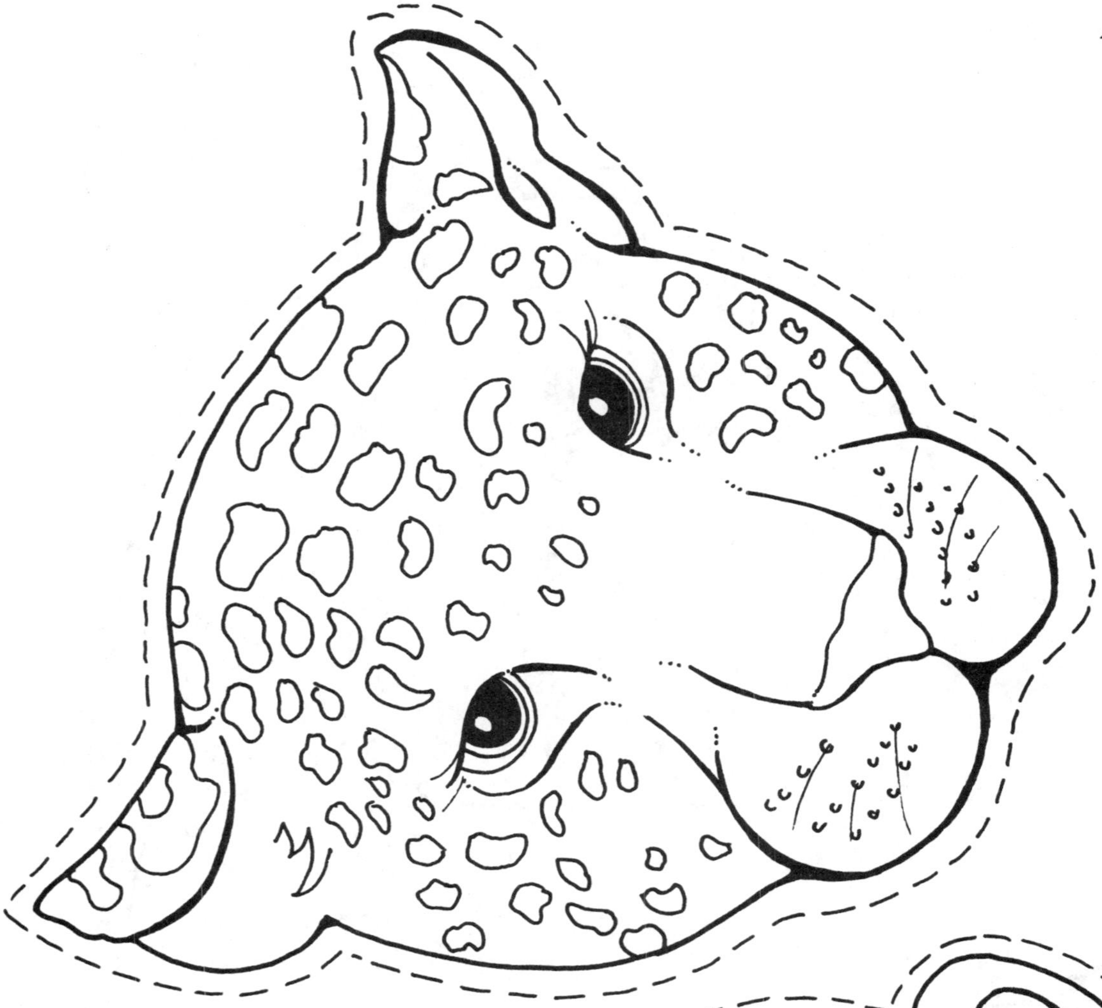

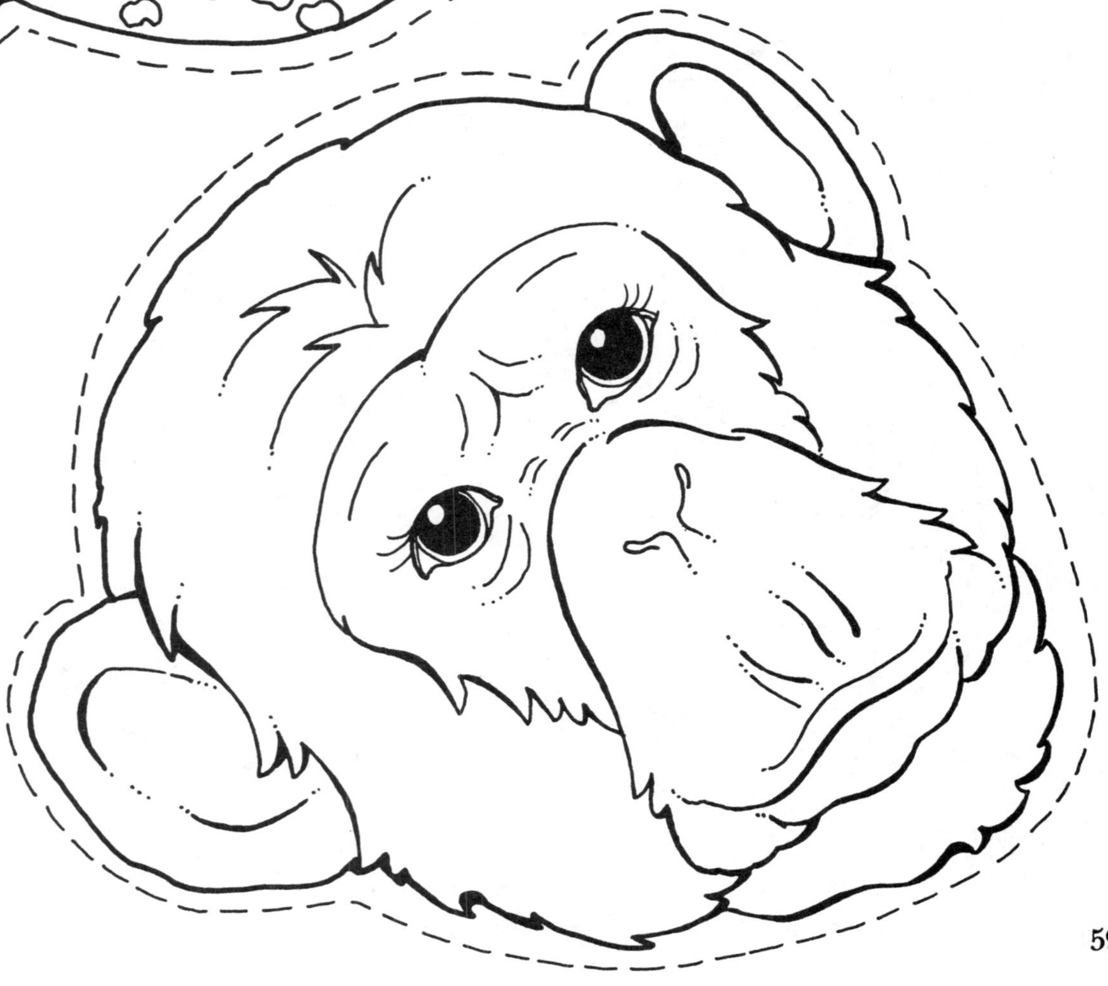

Giant Panda

We Learn All About Endangered Species © 1993 Fearon Teacher Aids

Black Rhinoceros

Endangered Species Pattern

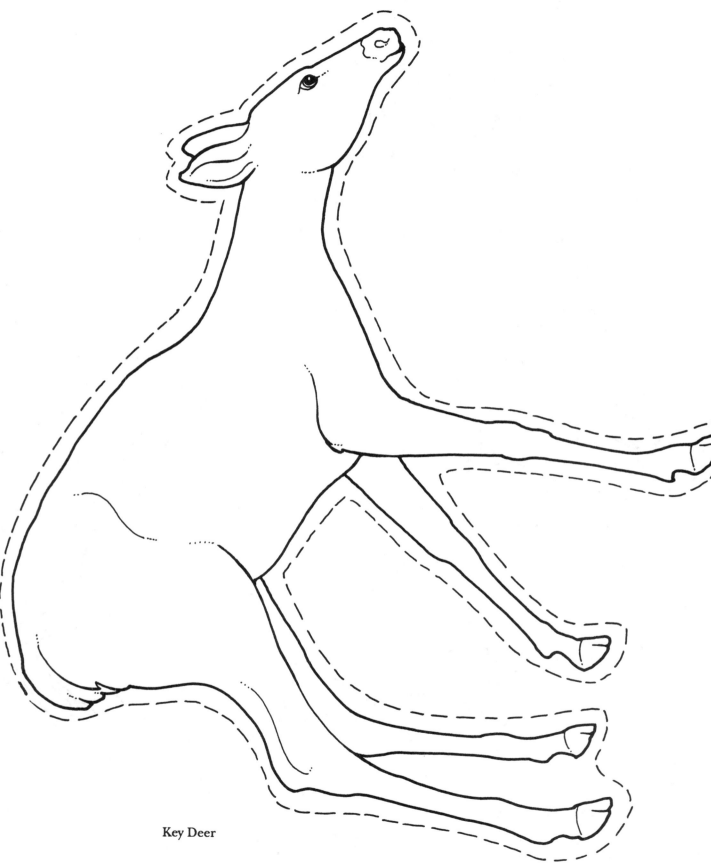

Key Deer

We Learn All About Endangered Species © 1993 Fearon Teacher Aids

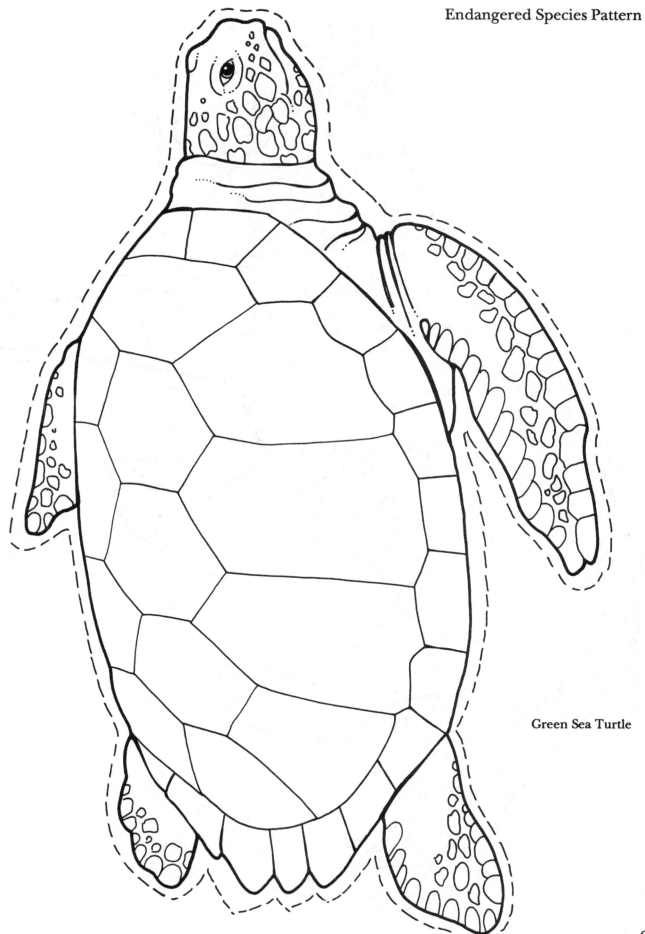

Endangered Species Pattern

Green Sea Turtle

We Learn All About Endangered Species © 1993 Fearon Teacher Aids

63

Endangered Species Pattern

Tiger

Wallaby

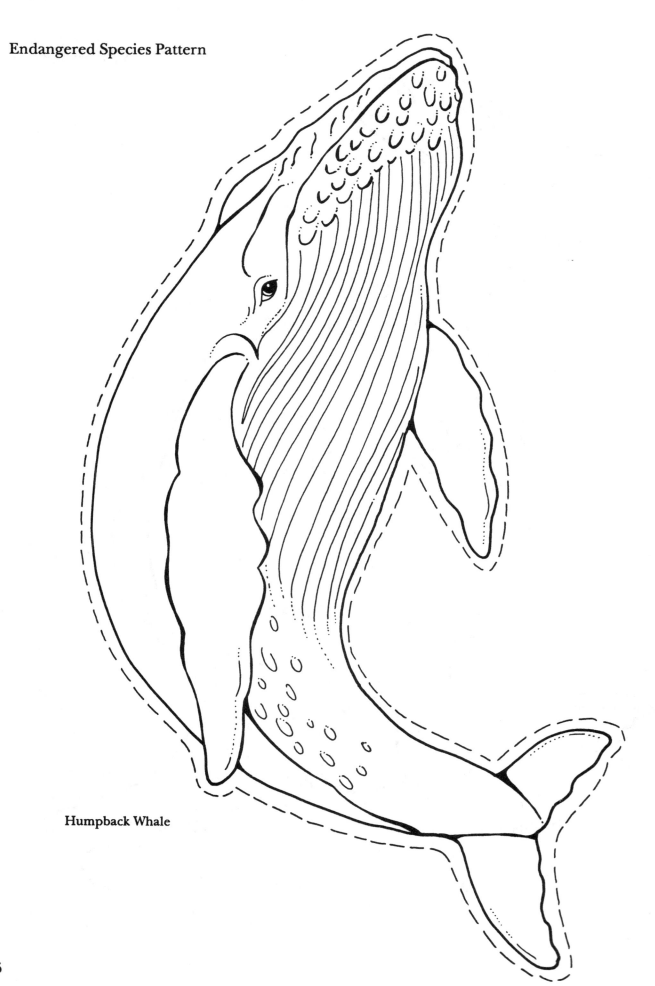

Humpback Whale

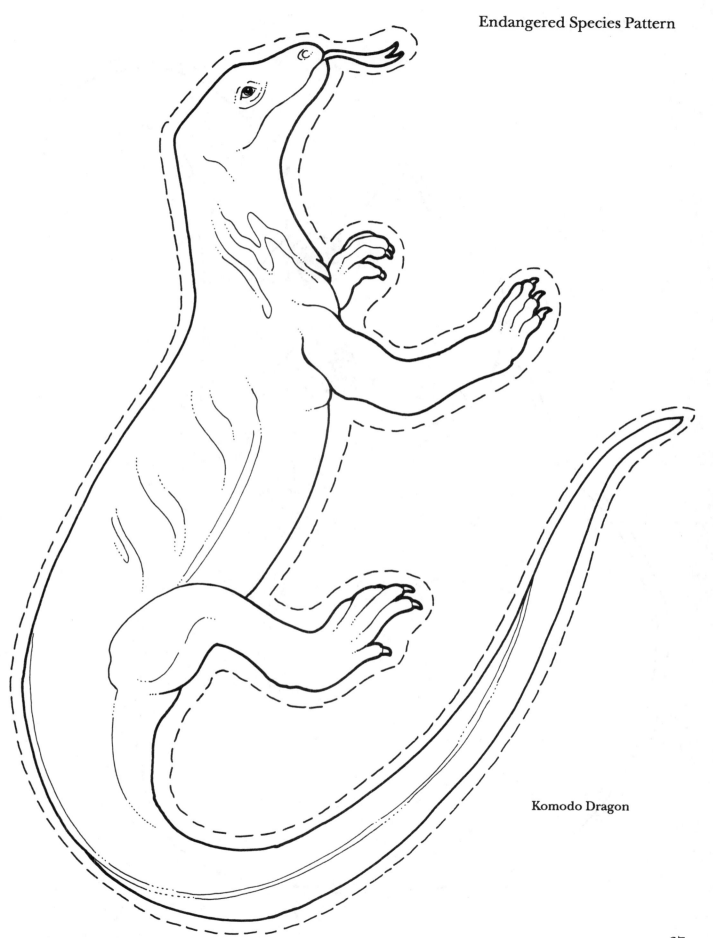

Komodo Dragon

Endangered Species Pattern

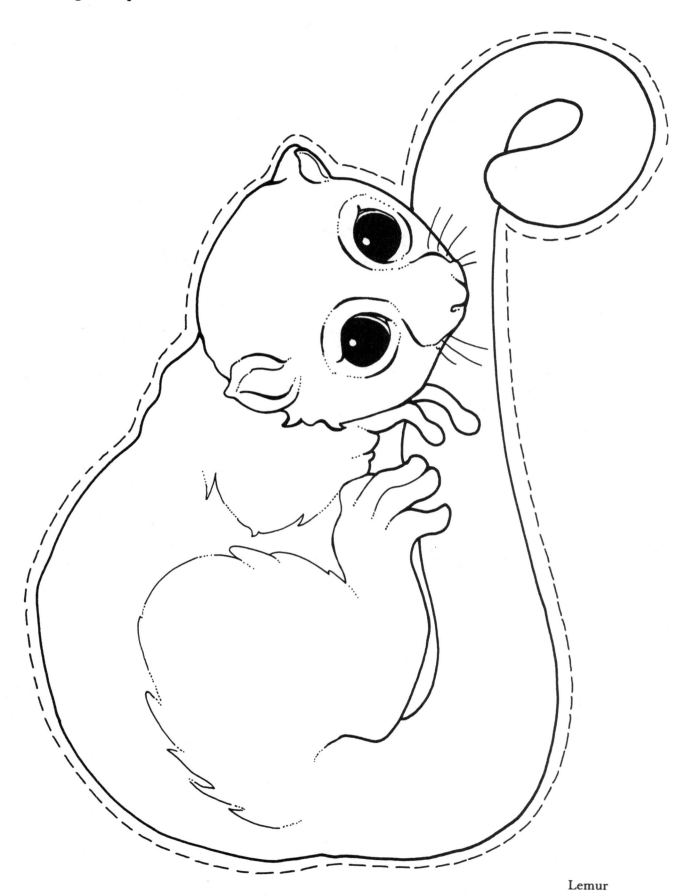

Lemur

We Learn All About Endangered Species © 1993 Fearon Teacher Aids

Sea Otter

Elephant Pattern

70

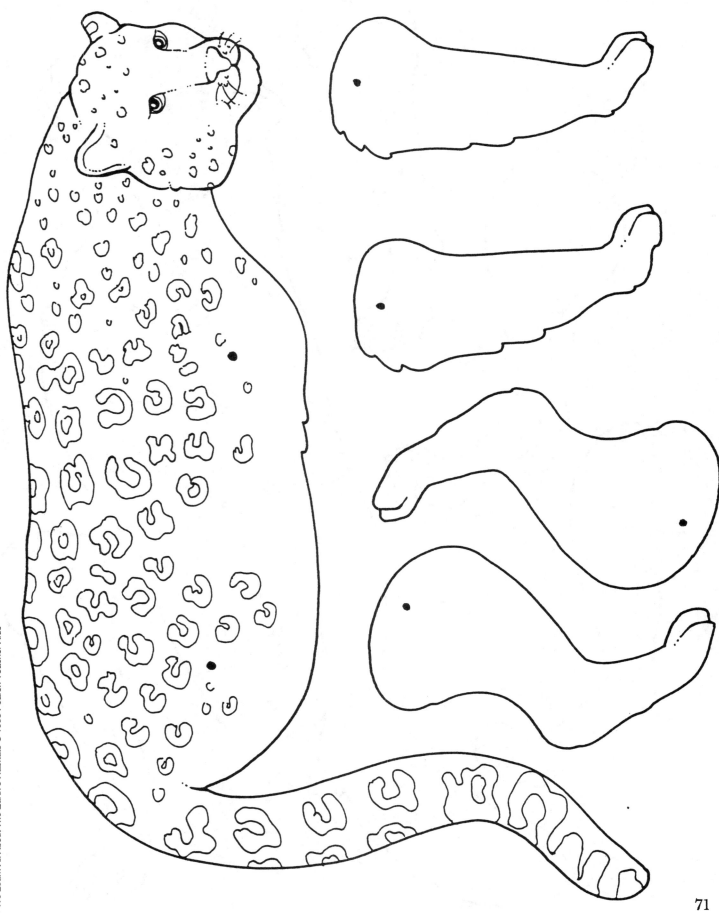

Timber Wolf Pattern

72

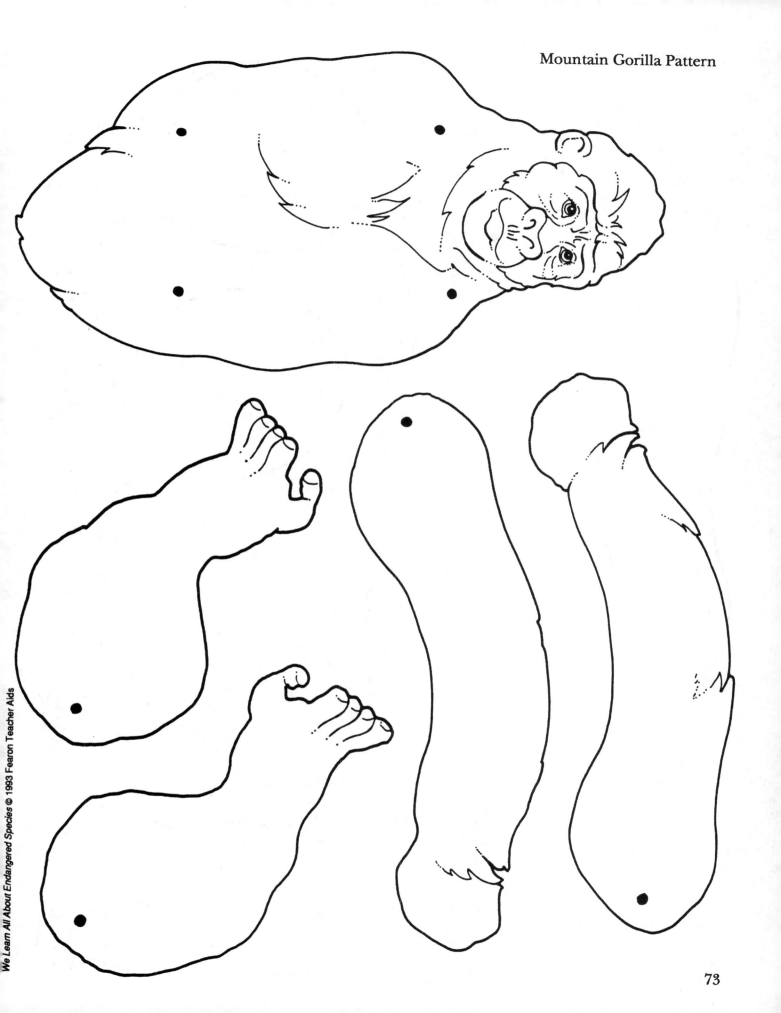

Mountain Gorilla Pattern

Polar Bear Pattern

74